JUDAICA
PRESS

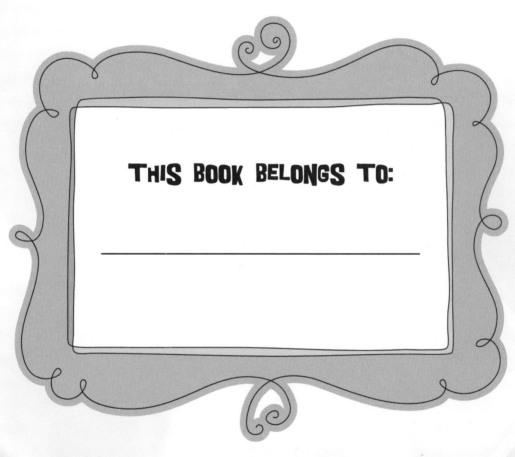

THIS BOOK BELONGS TO:

_____

I Give Tzedakah Every Day

by Naomi Shulman

I Give Tzedakah Every Day

ISBN: 978-1-60763-245-0

Author: Naomi Shulman
Editor and Art Director: Nachum Shapiro
Illustrator: DC Art

Published by:

The Judaica Press, Inc.
123 Ditmas Avenue / Brooklyn, NY 11218
718-972-6200 / 800-972-6201
info@judaicapress.com
judaicapress.com

Manufactured in China

I give tzedakah every day, a shiny coin or two.
I give it with a happy heart to help my fellow Jew.

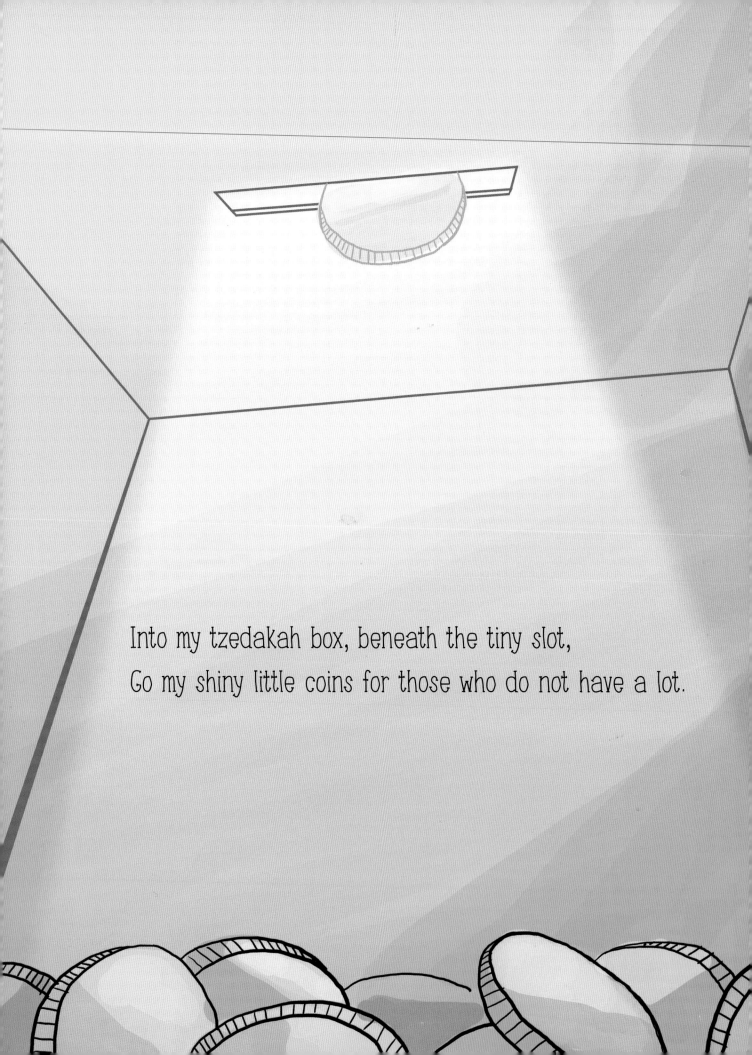

Into my tzedakah box, beneath the tiny slot,
Go my shiny little coins for those who do not have a lot.

Each and every single day I added coins with pride,
'Til one day it was full and no more coins would fit inside.

I told my mother, "Mommy — I can't fit another in!"

"That's okay ..." She took the box and all the coins within.

My mommy said, "Tzedakah is a very special deed.

It helps us become givers and it helps the ones in need.

But this mitzvah we are holding here has only just begun.
As long as it's inside the box, the mitzvah isn't done."

"Why is that?" I asked her. "Mommy, I don't understand.
Why is it not finished when my box is in your hand?"

"The tzedakah box is just the place where the tzedakah stays
'Til it can all be given out to help in different ways."

My mommy told me lots of things that all these coins could buy.
Like food and shoes and clothing, and children's school supplies.

"In order to make sure that they can buy these things and more,
We must give the coins to people, to help those who are poor."

"That's a great idea!" I jumped up and shouted loud.
"Let's give the coins away right now!" I said, so very proud.

"We'll take them to the store to help the people who can't pay.
We'll give them all the coins and make their problems go away!"

"Not so fast," my mommy said. "Now, this is a big deal —
We still want to be careful about how we'll make them feel.

Tzedakah is a mitzvah but it's surely not a game.
We don't want the ones we help to feel any shame."

"If they knew that we're the ones who gave them food to eat,

They might be too embarrassed when they see us on the street.

My mommy helped me give my pile of shiny coins away.
I didn't ask who got them, and my mommy didn't say.

The Rabbi took our coins and found a place for them to go.
He found someone who needed them, and that is all I know.

Now I give tzedakah even more than I did then.

My box is getting full of coins I'm putting in again.

I think I understand
   this special mitzvah even more
Now I think about the *feelings*
   of the people it is for.

We give tzedakah privately to help our fellow Yidden.

Tzedakah is the mitzvah that is best when it is hidden.

MORE JUDAICA PRESS BOOKS

How Mitzvah Giraffe Got His Long, Long Neck
By David Sokoloff

Rachel Golan   Rivka Landa
3-Minute Middos Stories for Children (and Parents, Too!)

Rachel Golan
MORE! 3-Minute Middos Stories for Children
Illustrated by Devorah Benedict

FIRST BIG BOOK OF WORDS FOR LITTLE KIDS
By Rachel Golan, author of 3-Minute Middos Stories
Illustrated by Dan Barlev
Ages 2 to 6

Rav Avigdor Miller and the Apple Seed
By Nachum Shapiro
Illustrated by Tova Katz

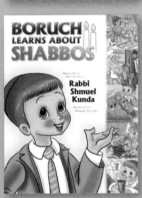

BORUCH LEARNS ABOUT SHABBOS
Rabbi Shmuel Kunda
Illustrated by Devorah Benedict

BORUCH LEARNS ABOUT PESACH
By Rabbi Shmuel Kunda

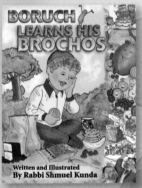

BORUCH LEARNS HIS BROCHOS
Written and Illustrated By Rabbi Shmuel Kunda

The Royal Rescue
By Rabbi Shmuel Kunda
Illustrated by Yoel Judowitz

WHERE ARE MY SHOE
BY ROCHEL BURSTYN

Let's Appreciate EVERYONE!
Bracha Goetz, author of Let's Stay Safe! and Let's Stay Pure

Aliza in Mitzvahland
by BRACHA GOETZ
Illustrated by TISHIA SUVAL

MY VERY OWN MITZVAH MOUTH
BRACHA GOETZ
ILLUSTRATED BY MALKA WOLF

MY VERY OWN MITZVAH HANDS
BRACHA GOETZ
ILLUSTRATED BY MALKA WOLF

MY VERY OWN MITZVAH FEET
BRACHA GOETZ
ILLUSTRATED BY MALKA WOLF

PHARAOH AND THE FABULOUS FROG INVASION
Written and illustrated by Oskar Warwar

Let's Tell the Story of The Beis Hamikdash
A child's first introduction to Tisha B'Av
By Sara Blau

The perfect introduction to Tefillah for kids!
I Daven Every Day
by Naomi Shulman

A charming story that teaches kids how to take responsibility for their mistakes
My Sister Has a Scooter
by Naomi Shulman

A CHILDREN'S CLASSIC
613 TORAH AVEN
Created by Cheryle Knobel and Rivkah